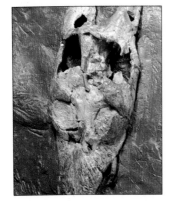

PREHISTORY

Text by Claudine Roland
Scientific Adviser:
Laboratoire de Préhistoire du
Musée de l'Homme
Translated by:
Ann MacDonald-Plénacoste

MSM

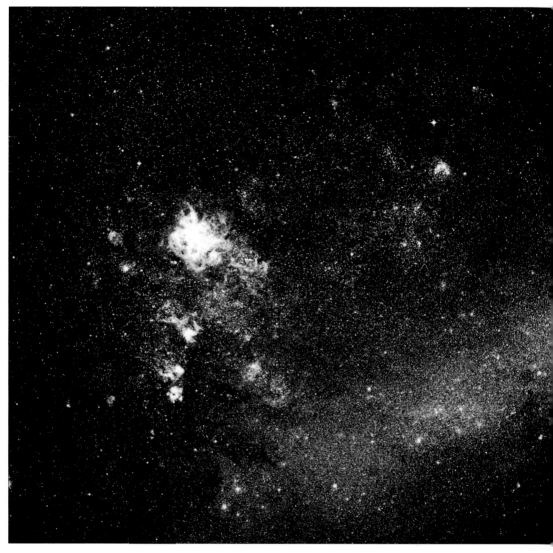

▲ *The Great Magellanic cloud. This galaxy "near" ours, is 170 000 light years distant… and is still moving further away. Since the Big Bang, the Universe has continued its expansion.*

▶ *Blue algae. Traces of this type of algae have been found in rocks 2 thousand million years old.*

◀ *Fronds of ferns fossilized from the Carboniferous (primary) era, Espace géologique du Château Queyras, Hautes-Alpes.*

THE ADVENTURE OF LIFE

Prehistory is concerned with the life of man from the appearance of his earliest ancestors until the discovery of writing, an adventure lasting some millions of years… a mere drop in the ocean of the history of our world! The birth of the Universe dates back to the Big Bang, 15 thousand million years ago. The galaxies were formed a few hundred million years later; amongst them, the Milky Way… After 10 thousand million years, one of many stars appeared on its periphery: the Sun with its planets – including the Earth. When it was formed 4.6 thousand million years ago, the Earth was simply an incandescent gaseous ball. On cooling, the gases became liquid, then solid, constituting the earth's crust with its oceans and continents. But there could be no life on the continents, since, to begin with, there was not enough oxygen in the atmosphere to form a protective ozone layer. The first forms of life, very simple unicellular organisms, probably developed in the oceans, a favourable environment for chemical exchanges, sheltered from harmful cosmic radiations. During the hundreds of millions of years which followed, vegetal and animal organisms multiplied and diversified. The race for complexity had begun…

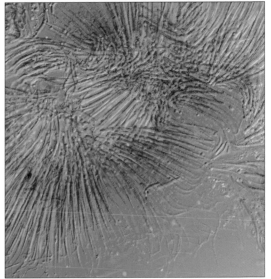

▲▲ *Ammonite fossil, Digne Musée de Géologie de Digne, Alpes-de-Haute-Provence. These molluscs were numerous during the secondary era.*

▲ *Brachyrotherium gallicum footprints, Musée Fleury, Lodève, Hérault. The traces left by this ancestor of the dinosaurs are over 200 million years old.*

▶ *Reconstitution of a Dromaeosaurida, Espéraza, Musée des dinosaures, Aude.*

▶▶ *Coelacanth, Musée de la Mer, Biarritz, Pyrénées-Atlantiques. This species was already in existence 350 million years ago.*

THE TERRIBLE LIZARDS

▲ *Diplodocus skeleton. Muséum National d'Histoire Naturelle, Paris. Why did the dinosaurs disappear? A fall of giant meteorites? Intense volcanic activity? A cooler climate? Competition between species? Ecological stress? For Philippe Taquet, dinosaur specialist, the causes are multiple, complex and spread out in time.*

At the beginning of the primary era, marine invertebrates abounded. Intense life proliferated in the oceans where primitive invertebrates appeared. Four hundred million years ago, fish dominated the seas. Timidly, the first terrestrial vertebrates, the amphibians, emerged from the waters... They already knew how to breathe the air of the atmosphere, but they still needed the aquatic environment, in particular for breeding. Reptiles, which were multiplying during the same period, laid their eggs, well protected by a hard shell, on the land. This enabled them to set about conquering the continent... the reign of the dinosaurs began more than 200 million years ago. There is one of these *terrible lizards* to suit every taste: from small ones, no bigger than a chicken, to giants as high as buildings. The herbivorous dinosaurs walked on two or four legs and had either reptilian hips (saurischiens) or bird hips (ornithischiens). The carnivores walked on two legs and all had reptilian hips. 65 million years ago, for some mysterious reason, the dinosaurs disappeared, leaving the coast clear for the discrete mammals... But it was not until some million years later that a primate appeared, which was not quite like all the others...

▲▲ *Footprint of a biped.*
3.7 million years old, it was
discovered in Tanzania.
Australopithecus or man?

▲ *Gorillas. These and the*
chimpanzees are our
"cousins".

▶ *Lucy's skeleton.*

◀ *Reconstitution of Lucy,*
Muséum National
d'Histoire Naturelle, Paris.
Small (1.05 metres) strong
with short legs and long
arms, she walked upright
and climbed trees.

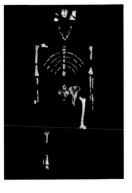

OUR ANCESTORS
FROM AFRICA

W e have the same ancestors as our close cousins, the gorillas and chimpanzees. But who were they? And when – and why – did the human line separate from that of the big apes? The answers are probably to be found in Africa... Approximately 18 million years ago, primates, the Proconsuls, abounded in the equatorial forest. Ten million years later, the rift, a gigantic crack to the East of Africa, collapsed. Its edges rose and mountains were formed, acting as a barrier against the rains. To the west of the rift, where the forest subsisted, the descendants of the Proconsuls became gorillas and chimpanzees. To the east, where the climate was drier, they became adapted to the savanna. They stood upright in order to be able to spot prey and danger more easily, and they ended up walking on two limbs... A plausible hypothesis: it was indeed in East Africa that the remains of the oldest Hominidae, called Australopitheci (*southern monkeys*), were found. In 1974, in Ethiopia, the oldest (3 million years old) and most complete skeleton was discovered: that of the Australopithecus, *Lucy* , already a biped. In 1993, in the same region, numerous fragments of bone were found, belonging to a new, even older species of Australopithecus (4.4 million years old), christened *Ramidus.*

7

▶ *A quartzite pebble from South Africa, Musée de l'Homme, Paris. The Homo habilis sharpened pebbles like this on one or both sides in order to give them a rough cutting edge. They were probably used more for crushing and cutting than for slicing. These tools, characteristic of the Oldoway civilization, are called, "choppers".*

◀ *The Verdouble and the Gouleyrous gorges, at the foot of the limestone cliff where La Caune de l'Arago is situated, Tautavel, Pyrénées-Orientales. Facing east near a water point and opening on to a valley rich in fauna, La Caune de l'Arago was an ideal shelter chosen by numerous Homo erectus.*

▶ *An Acheulean biface made of volcanic rock (size: 18 centimetres), Musée régional de Préhistoire, Orgnac-l'Aven, Ardèche. This biface was sharpened and touched up on both sides using another stone or a piece of wood.*

▶ *Trace of one of the oldest dwellings (380 000 years old), Musée de Paléontologie humaine, Terra Amata, Nice, Alpes-Maritimes. The Homo erectus mastered fire. Fire supplied heat and light, provided a means of cooking and therefore of preserving food, and made woodworking easier. It also gave men an opportunity to assemble in groups.*

▶▶ *Reconstitution of an Acheulean camp, Musée régional de Préhistoire, Orgnac-l'Aven, Ardèche.*

TOOLS AND MEN

The Australopitheci, who lived between the years - 6 million and - 1 million, perhaps mingled with the first representatives of the human race, the *Homo habilis*... their presence is certified in Africa as early as the year - 2.4 million, but could date back to the year - 3 million. They were bipeds with an almost doubled cranial capacity (almost 800 cubic centimetres), finer mandibles and more human teeth. They are called *skilled men* because they fashioned the first tools: simple sharpened pebbles. The site of Oldoway in Tanzania gave its name to the first human *civilization*. 1 700 000 years ago, a new hominidae appeared, first in Africa... This *Homo erectus* (upright man) was similar in weight and height to today's man, but he had no chin, his forehead was receding, above his eye sockets was a peak-shaped rim, and he had strong jaws and massive teeth! Having a larger brain (900 to 1 200 cubic centimetres), the *Homo erectus* made elaborate tools: bifaces and cleavers. The civilization associated with these tools is called *Acheulean* because it was defined at Saint-Acheul, a suburb of Amiens. Approximately 500 000 years ago, some *Homo erectus* discovered the way to produce fire, and how to tend it...

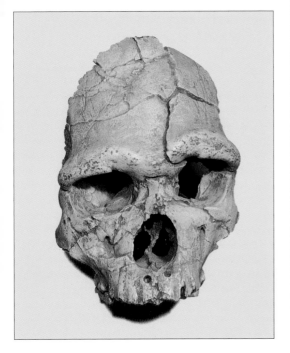

▲▲ *Skull of the Tautavel man. It was discovered in 1971 in La Caune de l'Arago, near this village in the Pyrénées-Orientales, during excavations organized by Henry de Lumley.*

▲ *Tautavel dwelling area. Debris of bones and tools show that the cave was occupied.*

▶ *A biface, Musée de Tautavel.*

◀ *Reconstitution of a Tautavel man driving off wolves, Musée de Tautavel.*

THE OLDEST EUROPEAN

Were the *Homo erectus* really the first explorers of the Earth? Certain clues would tend to show that the *Homo habilis* may have preceded them in Europe, but they were certainly the first to spread out systematically, taking advantage of interglacial periods to venture to the confines of Africa, Europe and Asia. Nomadic hunters, the *Homo erectus* settled in huts or caves, like at Tautavel, in the Pyrénées-Orientales. Thirty years of excavation work directed by Henry de Lumley have made it possible to form a more accurate idea of how these Tautavel men, who are among the oldest known Europeans, lived 450 000 years ago… They gathered in groups – each group consisting of about 20 individuals. Their camps depended on the movement of game. Armed probably with only simple stakes, they often tackled very fearsome animals: wolves, bears, cave lions, bison, horses, primitive musk oxen, stags, wild sheep, rhinoceros… Using tools knapped from quartz, flint, jasper, sandstone or limestone, they cut up their prey and broke open the bones to retrieve the marrow. The men of Tautavel had not yet mastered fire, and they have unfortunately left little trace of the arrangement of their dwellings.

▲ *An example of Levallois knapping, Musée des Antiquités nationales de Saint-Germain-en-Laye. This technique consisted of shaping a piece of flint around its circumference on its upper surface before detaching a fragment in the required shape.*

▶ *Reconstitution of a scene of mammoth hunting, Préhisto-Parc de Tursac, Dordogne. The mammoths, with woolly coats and very long tusks, abounded during the last glaciation. Before confronting them, the Neandertal men probably set traps for these fearsome animals.*

◀◀ *Primitive Man by the sculptor Dardé. This statue guards Les Eyzies, Dordogne. A portrayal inspired by the Neandertal man.*

▶ *André Leroi-Gourhan on the site of the Reindeer cave, Arcy-sur-Cure, Yonne. The excavations make it possible to establish the presence of Mousterian Neandertal men on the site.*

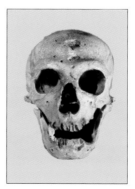

◀ *Skull of Homo sapiens neandertalensis. It was found in 1908 at La Chapelle-aux-Saints, in Corrèze.*

NEANDERTAL MAN

In 1856, in the valley of the Düssel, known as Neander, in Germany, the brain-pan and the bones of a very old male skeleton were discovered. At the time, the Neandertal man was considered to be a *brute* or an *idiot* because of his physique. He was thick-set, with a low forehead. A bony rim protected his eyes and the absence of cheek bones and chin made his face resemble a snout. And yet his skull, wide and drawn out towards the back, protected a brain with a capacity equivalent to that of modern man. Gradually, he was recognized as being a *Homo sapiens*, a wise man! Descending from a line of archaic *Homo sapiens* established in Europe some hundreds of thousands of years before, the Neandertal man lived from the year - 100 000 to - 35 000 from western Europe to Ouzbekistan and the Near East. In order to stand the great cold of the last glaciation, he took refuge in rock shelters or in huts made from mammoth bones. This master in the art of knapping flint invented a technique which enabled him to plan the shape of the pieces obtained. He is the main representative of the Mousterian civilization, defined on the site of Le Moustier in Dordogne. A great innovation was the fact that this wise man buried his dead, often with offerings: tools, animals, flowers…

▶ Soucy horses, reindeer antler, Magdalenian, Musée du Périgord, Périgueux, Dordogne.

◀◀ Magdalenian weapons and tools, Musée de l'Homme, Paris.

▶ Procession of bison from Chancelade, bone pendant, Magdalenian, Musée du Périgord, Périgueux, Dordogne. Homo sapiens sapiens was the most creative of the prehistoric men!

◀ Skull of the "old man" of Cro-Magnon, discovered in 1868 at Les Eyzies, Dordogne.

▲ *Necklace of perforated teeth from the Magdalenian, from the cave of La Marche in the Vienne, Musée de l'Homme, Paris. Homo sapiens already took care of his adornments…*

◀ *La Roque-Saint-Christophe. The valley of the Vézère in Dordogne is one of the most important places in prehistory. From Montignac to Bugue, the banks of this river and its affluents abound with sites formerly occupied by the men of the upper Paleolithic. In his book "The Colossus of Maroussi", Henry Miller notes with humour that "if Cro-Magnon man settled in this region, it is because he was extremely intelligent".*

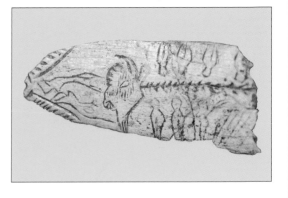

HOMO SAPIENS SAPIENS

The line of Neandertal men died out approximately 35 000 years ago. They did not disappear brutally, but were progressively replaced by other *Homo sapiens*, the *Homo sapiens sapiens* (doubly wise men…), with whom they probably cohabited for nearly five thousand years. These newcomers were from the Near East where their existence 100 000 years ago has been certified. They appeared in Europe 35 000 years ago. They are known as the men of Cro-Magnon, because it was at Cro-Magnon, near Les Eyzies in Dordogne that five skeletons, found in 1868, led to the definition of this human type. Cro-Magnon man was the first representative of the species to which we all belong: *Homo sapiens sapiens*. This *modern* man was not very different from us. He was quite tall with a straight forehead, prominent cheek bones and a marked chin. His skull protected a brain equivalent to ours. An excellent hunter, intelligent and skilful, he designed tools which enabled him to become more and more efficient. In order to be able to face the great cold of the last glaciation, he took shelter in huts built in the open air or in natural, well situated cavities. But above all, the *Homo sapiens sapiens* was the driving force of a veritable cultural revolution…

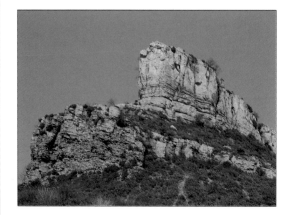

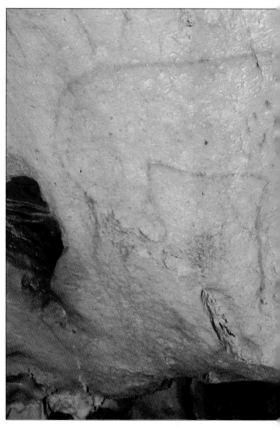

▲▲ *Solutré Rock, Saône-et-Loire. 20 000 years ago, hunters lived here. It gave its name to the Solutrean civilization and is therefore an eponymous site, from the Greek "epônumos": "which gives its name".*

▲ *Mas-d'Azil cave entrance, Ariège. The Azilian period was defined here.*

▶ *Vestiges of the troglodyte village of La Madeleine, Dordogne. The nearby rock shelter is the eponymous site of the Magdalenian period.*

▶▶ *Double burial from the Grotte des Enfants (Childrens' Cave), at Grimaldi, Musée d'Anthropologie préhistorique de Monte-Carlo. These skeletons, adorned with shells, may date from the Aurignacian period.*

▲ *A hyena and a spotted panther, the "Chauvet" cave, La Combe d'Arc, Ardèche. The numerous paintings and engravings from this cave, discovered near Vallon-Pont-d'Arc in December 1994, are masterpieces by the "Solutrean Leonardo da Vinci" according to Jean Clottes. Certain animals, like this panther, are portrayed for the first time.*

THE GOLDEN AGE OF PREHISTORY

Though the adventure of our earliest ancestors lasted for millions or hundreds of thousands of years, with the appearance of the *Homo sapiens sapiens* things happened faster! Civilizations coexisted in different places or followed on rapidly in the same place (the evolution of man taking place in a mosaic pattern rather than in a continuous line). Major findings are a regular occurrence in France which is especially rich in upper Paleolithic vestiges; it is therefore from these French sites that specialists have defined these civilizations which correspond to various levels as regards tools and artistic achievement. The Châtelperronian (from the year - 34 000 to - 30 000) identified in the Grotte des Fées (the Fairies' cave) at Châtelperron in Allier, is a transition civilization, developed by populations still belonging to the Neandertal period.

The first *Homo sapiens sapiens* belong to the Aurignacian culture (from the year - 33 000 to - 26 000) which takes its name from the cave of Aurignac, Haute Garonne. The Gravettian period (from the year - 27 000 to - 19 000) was defined from the site of La Gravette in Dordogne; the Solutrean (from the year - 20 000 to - 16 000) took its name from the site at Solutré en Saône-et-Loire; the Magdalenian (from the year - 16 000 to - 10 000) originates from La Madeleine in Dordogne, and finally the Azilian (from the

year - 10 000 to - 7 000) which comes from the Mas-d'Azil in Ariège. During the Châtelperronian period, men continued knapping pieces of flint, but they began to work tools on blades and to make instruments and weapons from the bones and antlers of cervidae. They built round huts propped up by mammoth tusks.
The Aurignacians developed the knapping of flint blades which they then adapted with oblique, often scaled retouches. They made endscrapers and burins. They worked bone a lot: awls, perforated batons and javelin points. The men of the Gravettian civilization, which developed in central and western Europe, were masters in the technique of blade knapping: the typical tool is a fine sharp flint blade, the *Gravette point*. During the Solutrean period, men excelled in the art of knapping flint.
The site of Solutré in particular has yielded up some magnificient javelin spears, known as laurel leaves. It was also at this time that the first eyed needles made of bone appeared. The Magalenians miniaturized and varied their stone tools. They created numerous bone objects (harpoons, spearthrowers…) which improved life for the hunters. The heating up of the climate, at the time of the Azilian period, resulted in the modification of the tools. Small endscrapers and points were numerous and miniaturization continued.

▲ *Reconstitution of the Mammoth bone hut, Mezerich (Ukraine). Le Thot, Thonac, Dordogne.*

◀ *Javelin points made from reindeer antler, Aurignacian, Musée de l'Homme, Paris.*

▼ *Pierced baton made from antler, Magdalenian, Laugerie-Basse (Dordogne), Musée de l'Homme, Paris.*

▲▲ *Stone and bone tools, Solutrean, Musée de l'Homme, Paris. On the left, the "laurel leaf" biface head, shaped by flat touches, polished after heat treatment.*

▲ *Gravettian tools, Musée de l'Homme, Paris.*

◄ *A spearthrower made from reindeer antler, called "faon à l'oiseau" Magdalenian, Bédeilhac cave, Ariège, Musée des Antiquités nationales de Saint-Germain-en-Laye. The spearthrower increased the power of the javelin throw.*

▶ *Azilian harpoon made from stag antler Musée de l'Homme, Paris.*

19

◀ *Aurignacian engraved block, Musée National de la Préhistoire, Les Eyzies, Dordogne.*

▶ *Ivory female head from Brassempouy, Landes, called "Hooded lady", Gravettian, Musée des Antiquités nationales de Saint-Germain-en-Laye. It measures 3.65 centimetres.*

▼ *"Venus with the horn" low relief from Laussel cave in the valley of the Beune, Dordogne, Musée d'Aquitaine, Bordeaux, Gironde.*

▶▶ *Ibex from the Pataud shelter, Les Eyzies, Dordogne, a sculpture in low relief from the Solutrean.*

▼ *Feminine figuration carved from a limestone block, Gravettian, Pataud shelter, Les Eyzies, Dordogne. This shelter, which opens out at the foot of the cliff of Les Eyzies, was systematically excavated from 1953 until 1963 by H.-L. Movius. Stratigraphic analysis has shown fourteen levels of dwelling, from the Aurignacian to the beginning of the Solutrean. A museum on the site shows this work.*

▶▶ *Mammoth tusk statuette called "Venus of Lespugue", Gravettian, Musée de l'Homme, Paris.*

THE FIRST ARTISTS

Prehistoric art was born as early as the Châtelperronian period. The hardy Neandertal hunters made ornamental pendants from animal bones or teeth and carved geometrical designs on tools or limestone blocks. However, figurative drawing did not make its appearance until the Aurignacian culture with the *Homo sapiens sapiens*: they decorated their everyday objects and portrayed improvised human forms, especially feminine ones, and some animals on blocks of rock. They also created necklaces and sets of jewellery from bone, ivory, shells or teeth. Art developed progressively during the Gravettian period. Engravings, sculptures and paintings from this period show even more schematized portrayals of animals. Elements of adornment became more and more varied. Feminine statuettes dating from this period have been discovered throughout the whole of Europe. Carved in ivory, bone or stone, they are in general representations of nude figures, in a standing position, with very rounded shapes, the features, feet and hands being scarcely outlined. They are called *Venus*, like the Roman goddess of love. But although they have often been regarded as symbols of fertility, their exact signification is not yet known. During the Solutrean period, exceptional works of art appeared, the most astonishing being

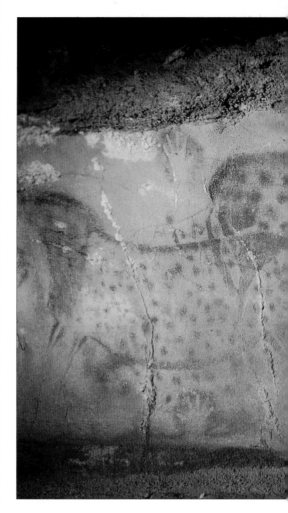

friezes engraved in half-relief. But it was definitely the Magdalenians who turned out to be the greatest prehistoric artists: they carved, sculpted and in particular painted the walls of a large number of caves in France and Spain with a mastery of technique and an evocative power which is still astounding today! Though they only had the scant light from the wavering flames of their lamps, these artists were not afraid to venture to the bottom of even the most obscure caves. The surfaces on which they chose to work were selected with care, and took advantage of possible reliefs in the rock. Sometimes they even prepared the surface to be decorated. In order to reach surfaces which were too high, they often had to build veritable scaffolding using tree-trunks or branches bound together with ropes. The engravers had flint points, blades and burins. Their incisions were often coloured. The sculptors too used flint tools: hammerstones, knives, burins, endscrapers... the *palettes* of the painters included black (charcoal or manganese oxide), white (kaolin) and above all reds, yellows and browns (ochre). These mineral substances were used as such or were ground in a stone mortar. The powder obtained was then diluted with water, marrow fat, the sap of certain plants or even urine or blood. To apply these colours to the walls, the artists by no

▲ *Horses and negative hands, Pech-Merle cave, Lot. These paintings were done between the Solutrean and the Magdalenian periods.*

◀ *Negative hand, Aurignacian or Gravettian, Gargas cave, Haute-Garonne. These hands are often "mutilated".*

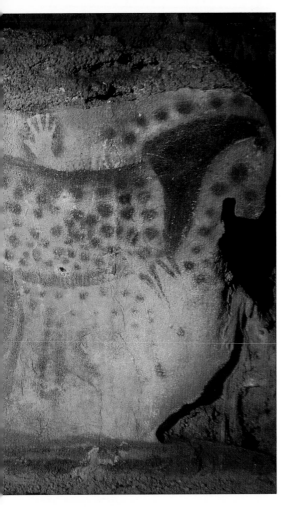

▲▲ *Engraved lion's head, Magdalenian, Combarelles cave, Dordogne. Nearly 300 engravings forming a superb bestiary were found here.*

▲ *Polychrome bison and reindeer, painting from the Magdalenian, Font-de-Gaume cave, Dordogne.*

◀ *Bison and horse, Niaux cave, Ariège. Due to difficulty in preserving this group of Magdalenian paintings ,certain have been reproduced in the Parc Pyrénéen d' Art Préhistorique.*

◀◀ *Bisons modelled from clay, Magdalenian, Tuc d'Audoubert cave, Ariège.*

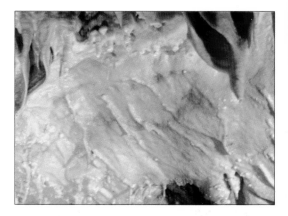

means lacked tools: their hands and their fingers; *crayons* of colouring materials (blocks of ochre for example); brushes made with vegetal fibre or animal hair; vegetal brushes or pads of moss or fur. They knew the technique of stencilling, as can be seen from the numerous hands found on the cave walls and which stand out *negatively* against a coloured background. They even invented the technique of *spray painting*: the colouring material was blown onto the rock using a hollow bone. Their favourite subjects: the animals from their environment. But they also drew mysterious signs and some human figures. Through his work, the prehistorian André Leroi-Gourhan was able to note that the composition of the works or art was highly organized: the same representations are found in the same places. According to P. Leroi-Gourhan, the bovine-horse association, the most frequent one, may symbolize the feminine-masculine couple. But prehistoric men did not, of course, indulge in art simply for art's sake: their works bear witness to their conception of life. The caves they decorated with such care were perhaps the sanctuaries of an already complex religion...

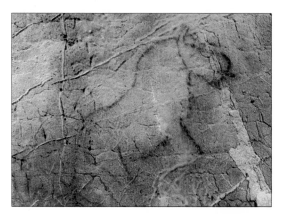

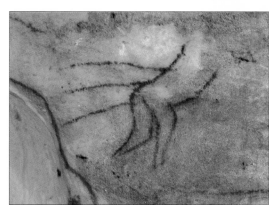

▲ Solutrean bovine from the cave of the Tête du Lion, Musée régional de Préhistoire, Orgnac-l'Aven, Ardèche.

◀ Villars cave, Dordogne. This "little blue horse", Magdalenian, was painted black, but the colouring changed.

▶ Mammoth and Ibex, Magdalenian, Rouffignac cave, Dordogne.

◀ Engraved bear, Magdalenian, Bara-Bahau cave, Dordogne.

▶ Mammoth, Solutrean, Chapelle des Mammoths, Pech-Merle cave, Lot. This cave is remarkable both for its natural beauty and for the quality of its parietal art.

◀ Oxocelhaya cave, Pyrénées-Atlantiques. This sturdy horse, from the Magdalenian period, resembles the famous basque pottok.

◀ The big penguin, Cosquer cave, Bouches-du-Rhône. In 1991, Henri Cosquer discovered this cave, the entrance to which is situated 37 metres below sea level in the calanque de Sormiou near Cassis. Its walls are decorated with negative hands but also with representations of animals dating from the Solutrean. Amongst the subjects, marine animals...

◀◀ Anthropomophic figuration, beginning of the Magdalenian, Cougnac cave, Lot.

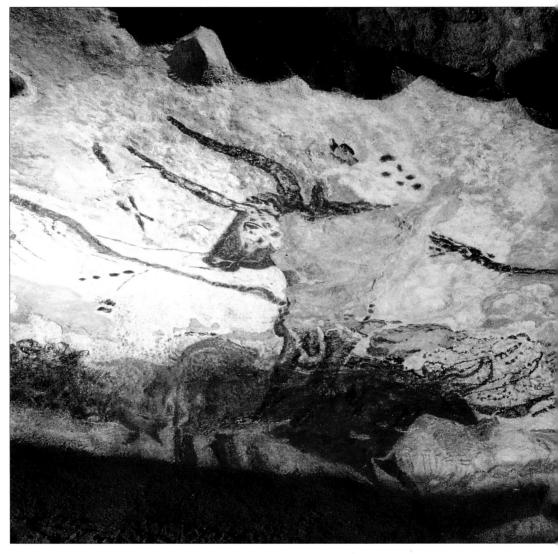

▲ *Lascaux, This famous bull justifies Abbey Breuil's famous exclamation "The prehistoric Sixtine Chapel!"*

◀ *Red and black cow and little jumping horses, Lascaux cave, Dordogne. Specialists wonder about the meaning of the sign drawn to the left of the cow.*

▶ *Lascaux. The artist who painted this gallop, has given the impression of depth by leaving white between the horse's neck and its left foreleg.*

THE MASTERPIECES OF LASCAUX

On September 12th 1940, near Montignac, Dordogne, four young boys playing at explorers, discovered a fabulous treasure: the Magdalenian frescoes and engravings of Lascaux, nearly 17 000 years old. Hundreds of metres of walls and roofs are covered with friezes of animals vibrating with life and colour. Bulls, bison, stags, horses... have been portrayed in movement with a remarkable sense of composition and coherence in realisation! Specialists unanimously consider this site to be one of the marvels of the prehistoric world. Opened to the public in 1948, the cave has welcomed an incessant flow of visitors. But its admirers gave off carbonic acid and water vapor, diffused calories and carried spores and bacteria in their clothing... In this enclosed environment, disease developed, seriously damaging the paintings. After vain attempts to remedy this, Lascaux had to be closed in 1963. But so as not to deprive the public of this masterpiece, part of the cave has been reproduced a few hundred metres away in a former abandoned quarry. The realisation of Lascaux II has made it possible to *re-invent* certain techniques used by the Magdalenian artists. Genuine reproduction guaranteed!

◀ *Dolmen des Pierres Plates (Flat Stones), Locmariaquer, Morbihan. A dolmen consists of a chamber limited by standing stones and topped by one or several stone slabs. Human remains were deposited in the chamber.*

▶ *Neolithic axes, Musée municipal de Préhistoire, Saint-Pons-de-Thomières, Hérault. Basic tools for farming populations, these axes consisted of a cutting blade in polished stone, a wooden handle and sometimes a sheath made from stag antler to fix the blade to the handle.*

▶ *Grain vase-silos, 4 200 years B.C. from the site of Les Bruyères at Saint-Julien-de-Peyrolas (Gard) Musée régional de Préhistoire, Orgnac-l'Aven, Ardèche. The Neolithic period saw the emergence of agriculture and ceramic art.*

◀ *Reconstitution of the Neolithic collective burial of La Caune de Bélesta, Château-musée de Bélesta, Pyrénées-Orientales.*

▶ *Reconstitution of the actual format of a Neolithic dwelling from the 6th millennium B.C., SAMARA, Somme. The Station d'Animation du Milieu et d'Archéologie de la Région d'Amiens provides an opportunity to discover the region's natural milieu and archeological wealth.*

▶▶ *Reconstitution of a weaving loom, end of Neolithic, SAMARA, Somme. During the Neolithic age material for clothing appeared with the invention of spinning and weaving techniques.*

FROM THE NEOLITHIC
TO THE METAL AGE

C ontrary to common belief, dolmens and menhirs were not the work of the Gauls. It was Neolithic man who erected these mysterious monuments called megaliths (big stones) throughout the world. Those found in France were erected mainly between 4 500 and 2 500 years B.C. But the "New Stone" Age began well before that. Approximately 10 000 years ago, the climate became milder and because of this, nature became more generous. Up until then, prehistoric men were *predators* who lived from hunting and gathering. They moved off to another area as soon as their environment could no longer provide sufficient resources. By inventing agriculture and breeding, they became food producers. This revolution began as early as the 11th millennium B.C. in a highly propitious region, the *fertile crescent* which stretched from the Eastern shores of the Mediterranean to the North of the Persian Gulf. One people, the Natoufians, actually settled in permanent villages in places where edible wild graminae , such as corn and barley, were abundant... Little by little, they began to gather and sow the grain and then to store their harvests in silos. They also began to rear animals: pigs, sheep, goats and oxen. During the 5th millennium B.C., in South America and Asia, the same techniques were invented

quite independently. In France, it was during the 6th millennium B.C. that agriculture made its appearance, under outside influence… At this time, men were still knapping tools from stone, but they polished the cutting edges (it is to mark the appearance of polished stone that the word "Neolithic" was created during the last century). These men sheltered their dead in dolmen chambers. Dolmens are composed of vertical slabs surmounted by one or several horizontal slabs. Their shape varies according to the region and the period. They are often covered with a tumulus of earth or stone, then called a cairn. Menhirs, simple standing stones of sometimes impressive size, were placed alone or grouped in "alignments". Cromlechs are menhirs set out according to very precise patterns: in a circle, half circle, rectangle… Various hypotheses have been put forward to explain the role of the menhirs: commemorative stones, boundary stones, religious symbols, astronomic markers… But they still retain their mystery intact. With the appearance of metal (in Europe, copper has been known since the 3rd millennium B.C. and bronze since the 2nd millennium B.C.) and then the invention of writing, man gradually entered History…

▲▲ *Engraved block from the Vallée des Merveilles (Valley of Marvels), Mont Bégo, Alpes-Maritimes. Over 100 000 engravings from the Bronze Age have been listed.*

▲ *Copper Age pottery left in place in the Foissac cave, Aveyron.*

▲ *Kermario alignments, Morbihan. 1 128 metres – the longest of Carnac.*

◀ *"Menhir statue" Filitosa, Corsica. Bronze or Iron Age.*

▶ *House in the village of Cambous, Hérault. Remains of the civilization called "Fontbouisse" (between 2 700 and 2 300 years B.C., the Copper Age). It was possible to speak of the Age of the Garrigues, sinces these men, breeders and farmers, were at the origin of the degradation of the original open forest.*

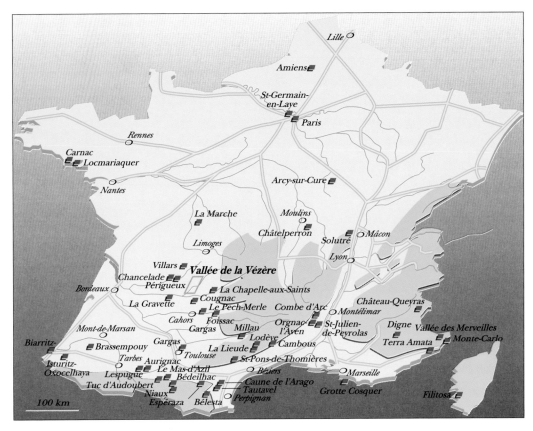

Lille
Amiens
St-Germain-en-Laye
Paris
Rennes
Carnac
Locmariaquer
Nantes
Arcy-sur-Cure
La Marche
Moulins
Châtelperron
Solutré
Mâcon
Limoges
Lyon
Villars
Vallée de la Vézère
Chancelade
Périgueux
Bordeaux
La Chapelle-aux-Saints
Cougnac
Château-Queyras
La Gravette
Le Pech-Merle
Combe d'Arc
Montélimar
Cahors
Foissac
Orgnac-l'Aven
St-Julien-de-Peyrolas
Digne
Vallée des Merveilles
Mont-de-Marsan
Gargas
Millau
Lodève
Cambous
Terra Amata
Monte-Carlo
Biarritz
Brassempouy
Gargas
La Lieude
St-Pons-de-Thomières
Isturitz-Oxocelhaya
Tarbes
Aurignac
Toulouse
Lespugue
Le Mas-d'Azil
Bédeilhac
Béziers
Marseille
Tuc d'Audoubert
Niaux
Caune de l'Arago
Tautavel
Grotte Cosquer
Filitosa
Espéraza
Bélesta
Perpignan
Foissac
Lodève
Cambous

100 km

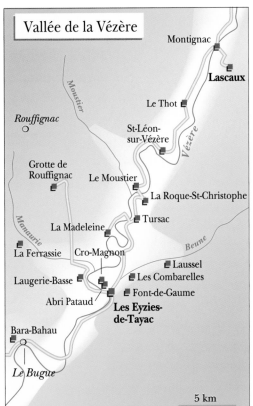

Vallée de la Vézère

Montignac
Lascaux
Le Thot
Rouffignac
St-Léon-sur-Vézère
Moustier
Vézère
Grotte de Rouffignac
Le Moustier
La Roque-St-Christophe
Manaurie
Tursac
La Madeleine
Beune
La Ferrassie
Cro-Magnon
Laussel
Laugerie-Basse
Les Combarelles
Abri Pataud
Font-de-Gaume
Les Eyzies-de-Tayac
Bara-Bahau
Le Bugue

5 km

CONTENTS

- The Adventure of Life — 3
- The Terrible Lizards — 5
- Our Ancestors from Africa — 7
- Tools and Men — 9
- The Oldest European — 11
- Neandertal Man — 13
- Homo Sapiens Sapiens — 15
- The Golden Age of Prehistory — 17
- The First Artists — 21
- The Masterpieces of Lascaux — 27
- From the Neolithic to the Metal Age — 29